I Love

Five Minute Stories

Read along with me

Brown Watson

ENGLAND

Contents

Written by Lisa Regan
Illustrated by Angelika Scudamore

First published 2019 by Brown Watson
The Old Mill, 76 Fleckney Road
Kibworth Beauchamp
Leicestershire LE8 0HG

ISBN: 978 0 7097 2726 2

Learning to Fly

Buster was nervous. It was his very first flying lesson today and he felt scared. His propeller wobbled and he thought he might cry. But Madame Roland, the flying instructor, took him under her wing.

'We will start gently,' she explained. 'Just a short trip, up into the sky and back down again. There is nothing to be afraid of. Just follow me and do what I do.'

Madame Roland trundled down the runway. Buster followed, watching very carefully. As they left the ground, Buster felt his heart do a loop the loop, but he lifted his wheels and stuck close behind her.

Wow! They were so high in the sky! Buster felt the wind rushing past, and couldn't take the smile off his face. Flying was amazing! He dipped one wing and wobbled slightly, then corrected himself.

Suddenly, Buster felt cold and
wet. He couldn't see a thing,
and he started to panic. Then
he heard the reassuring rumble
of Madame Roland's engines.
'Don't worry!' she shouted.
'It's only a cloud!'

Sure enough, they flew out and
into clear blue skies once more.
Buster grinned and speeded
up. As he approached the next
cloud, he knew what to expect.
'WHEEEEE!' he shouted.
'I am FLYING!'

Read these words again

follow

again

ground

behind

enough

panic

speeded

expect

nervous

flying

amazing

slightly

engines

carefully

What can you see here?

flag

aeroplane

rainbow

control tower

buildings

runway

15

The Special Pony

Reggie and Josie live on a farm, with cows in the faraway fields and ponies in the meadow outside their bedroom window. They love to stroke them and brush them and listen to them whinnying as darkness falls.

One evening, Daddy says he is worried about the youngest pony, Dazzle. He can feel strange bumps on her head and her back.
'I must call the vet in the morning,' he decides.

That night, Reggie hears a tapping on his window. He wakes Josie and they look out to see Dazzle gazing in. They quickly run outside.

As they get closer, they can see that Dazzle looks very different. She has sprouted wings, and a beautiful spiral horn is growing from her forehead. Dazzle is a unicorn!

The next day, Reggie and Josie stay close as the vet examines the little pony. She doesn't think the bumps are anything to worry about. She whispers in Dazzle's ear and feeds her a carrot.

Then the vet winks at them as she walks to her truck. 'Do you believe in unicorns?' she asks them. 'We definitely, definitely do!' they both say. 'Then take good care of her,' says the vet as she drives away.

Read these words again

look   pony

them   think

farm   walks

both   truck

feel   love

head   next

back   care

What can you see here?

brush

hills

bucket

cow

truck

A Dirty Trick

Max and Minnie were playing.
They had found a waterhole to
wallow in, and were splashing
around in the shallow water at the
edge. Minnie used her trunk to
scoop up some mud and
throw it at Max.

SPLAT! The mud sailed through
the air and landed on Max's
forehead. He laughed and picked
up an even bigger dollop to throw
in Minnie's direction.

Minnie saw the mud heading straight for her. She ducked down out of the way. The mud flew over her head, and hit Great Aunt Gladys right between the eyes. Uh-oh!

Great Aunt Gladys trumpeted loudly. She was NOT happy! She wiped the mud from her face and thundered towards the water. What were Max and Minnie going to do? Minnie thought quickly...

She ran into the water, pushing Max ahead of her. Great Aunt Gladys did not want to follow them. Deeper and deeper they went. Soon they were totally covered, and poked their trunks out of the water so they could breathe.

They waited until they hoped the coast was clear. When they peeped above the water, they could see Great Aunt Gladys lumbering off into the distance. Phew! They were nice and clean again, too!

bigger   wallow

loudly   quickly

water   coast

waited   breathe

sailed   distance

laughed   forehead

landed   direction

What can you see here?

fishes

leaves

mud

elephant

waterfall

flowers

A Big Day Out

Lila was very excited.
Her mummy was taking her
to the city for the day.
They boarded the train and
watched the fields zoom past.

As they left the station, Lila
gasped at the busy crowds.
'Mummy, can we go to the
museum?' she asked, and they
began to walk. Lila spotted
a big bus. 'Mummy, can we go
on a bus?' she pleaded.

Inside the museum, Lila gazed at all the animals. 'Mummy, can we find a dinosaur?' she asked. 'They're my favourite.' Mummy took her hand and set off down the corridor.

'Mummy, can we visit the big tower?' Lila asked next. 'Yes, but first we need some lunch,' replied mummy. 'Ooh, please can I have a cookie?' begged Lila. After lunch, they walked to the tower. 'Mummy, can we climb to the top?'

DINOSAUR

The sun shone brightly and Lila was very hot. 'Mummy, please can I have a drink? And then can we go to the park?' They headed to the park with their drinks in their hand. 'Mummy, can we feed the ducks?'

Soon it was time to go home. 'Mummy, can we just play on the swings? And will you push me high?' Lila climbed into a big, round swing. Mummy pushed her gently, and Lila fell asleep. She was exhausted!

Read these words again

top	swing
day	drink
walk	lunch
park	tower
ducks	asleep
city	corridor
train	fields

What can you see here?

duck

roundabout

swings

pond

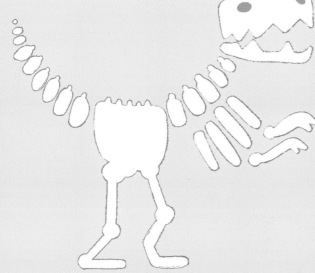

bones

bulrushes

On the Move

Billy has a new scooter. 'Wheeeee!' he calls as he zooms past. 'Look at its cool wheels!' Billy skids to a stop to let everyone admire his scooter.

Carmen has her sister's old bike. She feels very grown up, riding on her own. 'My wheels are so big!' she declares. 'And they have shiny discs that flash when I cycle along!'

Prajit whooshes past on his skateboard. 'Well, my wheels don't look much, but they make me go really fast!' he shouts. 'And I have more wheels than you!'

Alex also has four wheels on his go-kart. He pedals as fast as he can and picks up speed down the hill. 'I'm fast, too!' he hollers. 'Wahoooo!'

Stella whizzes past and waves at them all. She is going so fast, they can't even see what she is riding on. She does a quick turn and zooms back towards them. They all clap their hands as she comes to a graceful stop.

'I have more wheels than any of you!' she laughs. 'And I love it!' She twirls around in a circle and then skates off backwards. The friends all clap again. Stella is really clever!

Read these words again

fast   four

flash   turn

clap   when

speed   circle

hill   much

down   make

stop   calls

What can you see here?

helmet

bike

rollerskates

go-kart

scooter

skateboard

Play Time

Susie Saurus wanted to play. But no one would play with her. 'Please will you play hide and seek?' she asked. But her neck reached so high that she could easily see where all of her friends were hiding.

She asked Trudi Triceratops if she could join in her skipping game. But Susie's tail was so enormous that they couldn't find a skipping rope long enough. She got tangled all the time.

Victor Velociraptor was
playing ball with Vanya.
'Can I play, too?' asked Susie.
But she was so tall that she
grabbed the ball every time.
The others got bored and
wandered off.

Susie found Izzy Iguanodon
playing hopscotch by herself.
'Ooh, do you want some
company?' she asked. Izzy was
happy to have a friend — except
that Susie couldn't fit her big feet
inside the lines.

Hector Hadrosaur was building a den. 'I'll help!' said Susie. 'I can carry heavy branches, and pile them high!' But Susie's thunderous footsteps shook the ground, and knocked down the den every time.

Susie lay down and began to cry. Then Gabby Gallimimus and her family appeared. They jumped on Susie's back and slid down her tail. 'Hurray!' they squealed. 'You do make a good slide, Susie!'

Read these words again

began   skipping

wanted   appeared

jumped   company

heavy   except

ground   reached

hiding   would

inside   enormous

What can you see here?

flower

red dinosaur

leaves

vine

foliage

skipping rope

Caught in the Act

Bot was a robot. He lived in the bedroom of a little boy called Kieran. But Bot was a naughty toy, who liked to cause mischief in the night time.

He mixed up all the DVDs so they were in the wrong cases. He took the batteries out of the dinosaur so its eyes wouldn't flash. He turned up the volume on the electric organ so it was really loud.

Now, Kieran was a clever boy and he thought he knew who was to blame. One night, he curled up under his covers and pretended to be asleep. Really, he was awake, and watching.

He heard a whizz and a buzz as Bot whirred into action. Kieran peeped out from his bed and saw the cheeky robot heading for the jigsaw that lay, nearly finished, on the floor.

As quick as a flash, Kieran flicked a switch on a remote controller. His toy crane rolled across to where the robot stood, just about to steal a vital piece of the puzzle.

The robot bleeped as the crane swung down and scooped him up. 'Got you!' laughed Kieran, and he swung the crane around and left the robot in midair. And that's where he hangs every night, to keep him out of mischief!

Read these words again

quick

remote

asleep

laughed

action

cheeky

jigsaw

under

awake

bedroom

mischief

naughty

dinosaur

electric

What can you see here?

window

ball

jigsaw puzzle

dinosaur

bed

books

Mrs Tracey's Trousers

Mrs Tracey is everyone's favourite teacher. She is always happy and smiling and sings little songs to herself. And she loves to wear different clothes. On Monday, she wears big blue bell-bottomed trousers.

On Tuesday, Mrs Tracey wears purple paisley pantaloons. They are quite something else! The children can't wait to see what she wears on Wednesday.

They aren't disappointed.
On Wednesday she wears cute
cropped trousers with cucumbers
on. Hmm, very curious,
Mrs Tracey!

On Thursday, Mrs Tracey has an
important meeting. She wears a
smart striped suit – with stars
down the sleeves, of course.

On Friday, Mrs Tracey stands at the window to welcome her class. She is wearing flappy, flowery flares. The children look around, puzzled. Mrs Tracey says hello.

'Oh, there you are!' laugh her class. 'Mrs Tracey, we didn't see you standing there. You are camouflaged against the curtains!'

Read these words again

class   quite

happy   else

songs   cute

big   laugh

stars   blue

Friday   smart

there   look

What can you see here?

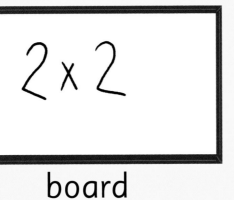

board

plant

clock

poster

globe

bookcase

Alfie's Adventure

Alfie loved to explore the field behind his house. He ran through the long grass and sat on the big, low branches of his favourite tree. He lay on his tummy and watched the bugs climbing up the flower stalks.

As Alfie listened to the wind in the plants, he heard another noise. As he looked around, he gave a little yelp. He was eye to eye with a little squirrel with bright eyes and a twitchy nose!

'Hello,' said the squirrel. 'I'm Hazel. Pleased to meet you!' Alfie didn't know what to say. 'Erm, hello,' he stuttered. 'I'm Alfie.' Hazel told Alfie that she had something for him to see.

She bounded off into the grass, her big bushy tail bouncing behind her. Then she stopped and looked back. 'Well, are you coming or not?' she asked. Alfie stumbled to his feet in a daze.

Hazel the squirrel led Alfie to an enormous tree. 'After you,' she said, and beckoned to a small opening in the trunk. Alfie poked his head inside and saw a tiny staircase spiralling upwards.

Alfie climbed up and up, higher and higher. As the sunlight grew brighter, the staircase opened onto a little platform at the very top of the tree. 'Wow!' gasped Alfie, looking out over the whole town. 'I'm on top of the world!'

Read these words again

tree

head

town

nose

small

feet

daze

bugs

eye

tail

higher

noise

whole

sunlight

What can you see here?

stairs

spider

ladybird

squirrel

flowers

dragonfly

How to Make an Ogre Happy

Once upon a time, there was an ogre. He lived in the biggest house in the village, with an enormous garden. All the children wanted to play there, but he was too grumpy to let them.

One day, a little boy kicked his football over the ogre's garden wall. The ogre saw it and roared, and kicked it straight back over the other side. He didn't want to play ball.

A little girl was sitting nearby, reading. A sudden gust of wind snatched up her comic, and blew it directly towards the ogre's garden. Oh no! What should she do? Timidly, she rang the doorbell.

The ogre answered the door and growled at her. In his hands were the shredded pages of the comic. He stuffed one page into his mouth, chewed it, and slammed the door. The little girl burst into tears.

Two little boys were walking past the ogre's garden, practising their tunes for the concert. As they reached his garden wall, they grew quiet so they wouldn't make the ogre angry.

The ogre wasn't roaring or growling, but he was whistling. Nervously, they played their tune again. The ogre whistled in time. Now, he always attends the village concerts, and sometimes even sings along. He loves music!

Read these words again

gust
garden
kicked
concert
roared
directly
village

slammed
chewed
whistling
nervously
quiet
straight
enormous

What can you see here?

audience

ball

cat

maracas

singer

ogre

Telling the Truth

Something bad has happened in the garden. Mummy looks out of the window and sees her flowers lying on the floor. Oh no! Those are her favourites, and she waters them lovingly every night.

She stomps outside to find out more. 'Freddie! Freya!' she shouts, and she sees two pairs of eyes peeping from behind the shed. 'Come out here this minute!'

'What happened? And who did it?' asks mummy with a tear in her eye. Freddie points at Freya. 'She did it! She kicked the ball and it smashed the pot.'

Mummy turns to Freya. 'Well?' she asks, 'what's your story?' Freya gasps and glares at Freddie. 'He did it! He was playing football and kicked it too hard!'

Mummy looks from one child to the other, and then sits down. 'Now I don't know who to believe,' she sighs. Both children hang their heads in shame. 'I did it,' they say at the same time.

Now mummy realises what has happened. They were both playing football, and so they were both involved. 'Well,' she says. 'You may be naughty, but at least you don't tell lies!'

Read these words again

out	floor
come	both
same	ball
time	hard
lies	story
shed	tell
two	who

What can you see here?

hanging basket

bees

window

door

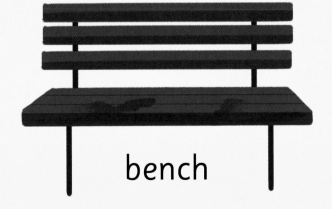

bench

plant pot

Time for Tea

Jake was very excited. His friend Cameron was playing at his house. Jake had a big secret to share with him. He ran to the bottom of the garden and proudly showed off the entrance to a small tunnel.

Jake got down on his knees and began to crawl inside. 'Follow me!' he shouted to Cameron. 'It is the best thing EVER – better than you could even think of in your best ever dreams!'

Cameron followed Jake down the tunnel. As they neared the end, the light grew bright and they could hear music. They crawled out, and straight into a circus. 'Is this real?' asked Cameron.

'It's magic!' explained Jake. 'Every time I crawl through, it is a different place at the end. Last week, it was Donut Land, and the time before that it was Pyjama Land, where you never have to get dressed!'

The two boys stayed at the circus for a long time. They laughed at the clowns, and gasped at the acrobats flying through the air. Then Jake said they really should go home.

Cameron asked if he could visit again soon. He loved the magic tunnel! And the next time they crawled along it together, they landed straight in Tea Party Land. That was a big hit, as you can imagine!

Read these words again

magic   showed

secret   crawled

music   imagine

friend   bright

shouted   laughed

dreams   straight

tunnel   pyjama

What can you see here?

cookies

drink

ice cream

popcorn

cake

sandwiches

Books aren't Boring

Uncle Joe is coming to stay.
He usually brings a present for
Maisie and Matt, so they are very
excited. As he walks through the
door, they rush to meet him and
give him a big hug.

Uncle Joe laughs and ruffles their
hair. 'Wow! You've grown!' he
exclaims. Then he hands over a
large, rectangular package and
winks at them. 'It's not all it seems,'
he promises. They tear off the
paper excitedly.

Maisie and Matt smile politely.
The present is a book, and they
already have lots of books.
They were hoping for a game.
They place it on the shelf and
join their family for dinner.

When bedtime comes, Uncle Joe
whispers to the children. 'Don't
read the book before bed,' he
says. 'It might keep you awake.'
The children aren't too bothered
anyway. They rub their eyes
sleepily and snuggle under
the covers.

Weeks after Uncle Joe's visit, they notice the book on the shelf. It is raining outside, so they decide to take a look and pull the book onto the floor. As they open up the cover and begin to read, an amazing thing happens. The characters in the story come to life!

Now the children read their magic book every day. Each story brings a new adventure, and they visit faraway places. Books aren't boring at all!

Read these words again

walks

book

story

new

hair

game

open

large

stay

door

smile

awake

floor

magic

What can you see here?

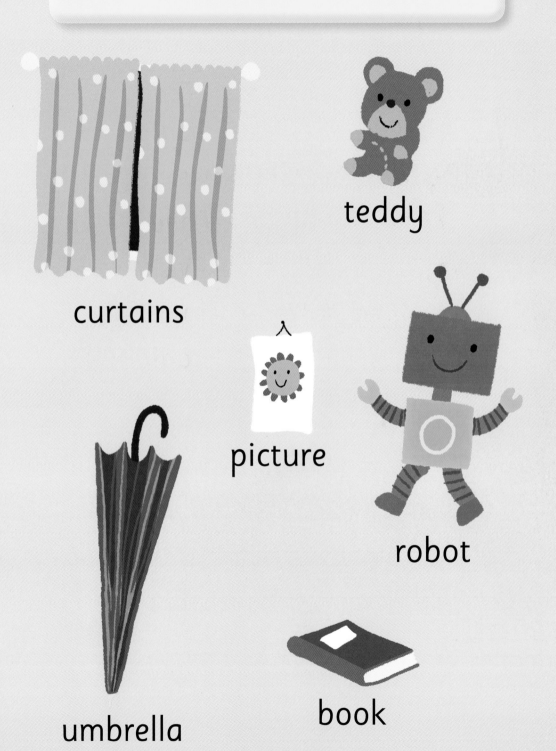

curtains

teddy

picture

robot

umbrella

book

Flowers for Mummy

Fee and Dan are shopping. As they run down the street, Fee sees some beautiful flowers in one of the shops. 'Dan! We should buy some flowers for Mummy's birthday tomorrow!' she whispers.

They look in the window. 'Those flowers cost a lot of money,' says Dan. 'I don't think Mummy would want us to spend so much. Let's see what else we can find.'

They skip past the fountain, which is surrounded by gardens full of different blooms. 'Can we give these flowers to Mummy?' Fee asks. But the gardener would be very angry if people picked these ones.

They walk back towards their house. 'Would Mr Green give us some flowers from his garden?' asks Fee as they pass the glorious garden next door. 'I think we would get in big trouble if we don't ask him,' worries Dan.

Mummy makes their lunch and leaves them to eat. 'I have an idea,' says Dan, and runs into the playroom. He returns with a big box. Fee's eyes light up.

Together, Dan and Fee make a huge bunch of flowers from tissue paper. They are all sorts of bright colours. Even better, these flowers don't need water, and will never die. Mummy will love them!

Read these words again

down

better

eat

much

find

paper

else

next

full

skip

street

shops

think

back

What can you see here?

scissors

glue

fountain

flowers

Ted's Big Adventure

Charlie loves his teddy very much. Today, before he went to school, he sat Ted on the windowsill so he could look outside. Charlie doesn't want Ted to be bored when he is on his own.

Ted watches the people and cars, when suddenly, a gust of wind picks him up and blows him to the ground. Help! Ted lies in the grass and stares at the sky. What can he do to get home?

Poor Ted doesn't like being here alone. A big buzzy dragonfly hovers next to his ears and makes him afraid. He wishes he was back in Charlie's bedroom.

The sky goes dark as a huge bird flies overhead. It sees Ted and swoops down to grab him. With a flap of its giant wings, it carries him through the air and then drops him to the floor.

Now Ted is frightened. How will
he ever get home? He can hear
cars zooming past, and does
not know where he is.

Ted trembles as the sky darkens
again. This time, it is a human
looming over him. 'Ted!' says a
voice he knows. 'How did you
get onto the drive? Let's take you
back inside for Charlie.' It is Dad,
and Ted has been rescued!

Read these words again

here   home

hear   cars

back   where

sky   help

wind   time

look   again

wings   dark

What can you see here?

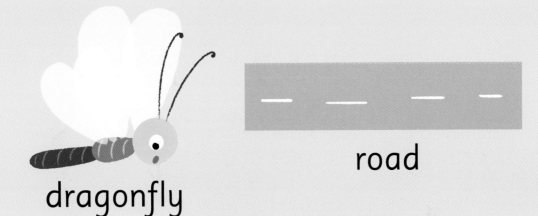

dragonfly

road

grass

car

motorbike

A Helping Hand

'5-4-3-2-1...blast off!' shouted
Bradley, as his rocket engines
fired and launched him into space.
He looked out of the window as he
climbed higher, leaving Earth
far behind.

Bradley poured a glass of milk,
and settled down to watch a movie.
It was going to be a long trip.
Then he felt a judder, and a wobble,
and heard odd noises coming from
the engine room. Hmmm...

He would have to do an emergency landing. Bradley checked his space map to see if there was a planet anywhere near. He spotted a large, red planet with a big ! in the middle of it.

'Does that mean it isn't safe?' Bradley wondered. But he had no choice — nowhere else was close enough, and he had to fix his engine problems. He steered the rocket towards the planet.

He peeped out of the window nervously. Would the aliens here be big and scary, with sharp teeth or tentacles full of suckers? Would they gobble him up before he even had chance to ask for help?

Bradley crossed his fingers and hoped for the best. Luckily, the aliens here didn't have tentacles. Instead, they had hands like tools, so they could easily mend his engine. Thank goodness for that!

Read these words again

glass	planet
hoped	towards
scary	instead
engine	noises
red	poured
easily	climbed
choice	tentacles

What can you see here?

pink alien

planet

map

dog

purple alien

rocket

Jiya's Mega Milkshake

Jiya has an empty tummy. She isn't sure if she is hungry or thirsty. She decides to make a drink that is full of good things to fill her up.

She finds the largest glass in the cupboard and places it on the table. Then she looks in the fridge. 'Hmm, milk is good for you,' she says, and pours some in the glass.

'Chocolate spread is yummy,' she thinks, as she rustles through the jars. She plops two spoonfuls into her drink.

'I do like bananas,' she smiles, and squishes one into pieces before dropping it into the glass. She gets a long spoon and stirs it all around. Then she spies her favourite breakfast hoops and sprinkles some on top.

The drink looks too gooey and sticky, so Jiya goes back to the fridge. 'Orange juice!' she declares, and adds a big splash to the mixture.

Mummy comes into the kitchen. 'Oh, Jiya!' she says. 'Would you like some help?' Mummy pours Jiya's drink into a smoothie maker. 'Press that button,' she says, 'to create your tastiest invention ever!'

Read these words again

into	comes
fill	some
good	then
looks	drink
glass	one
milk	press
too	back

What can you see here?

sink

jug

banana
peel

blender

drawers

143

Maddie's Lucky Day

Maddie and her mummy were going to visit Grandma. As they walked down the road, Maddie noticed something shiny on the pavement. 'Ooh, a penny!' said her mummy. 'That will bring you good luck.'

Maddie picked up the penny and skipped ahead. Suddenly, a black cat ran in front of her, and Maddie yelped in surprise. 'Don't worry,' said Mummy. 'Black cats are meant to bring good luck as well!'

Mummy held Maddie's hand as they crossed the road to the fields near Grandma's house. Two magpies were chattering on the fence. Mummy laughed. 'Some people think that's a lucky sign, too!'

Maddie smiled. She liked lucky days. She kicked through the long grass and poked the pretty flowers with her shoe. Mummy told her that they were clover flowers, and bees loved them.

'And guess what?' said Mummy. 'If you find a four-leafed clover...' Maddie knew the answer already. 'It will bring good luck!' she laughed, and started searching.

When Grandma opened the door, Maddie handed her a four-leafed clover and told her all their lucky signs. 'Well,' said Grandma. 'It is your lucky day – and I've baked your favourite cupcakes, too!'

Read these words again

baked   noticed

shiny   pavement

flowers   crossed

skipped   fields

ahead   searching

surprise   knew

walked   guess

What can you see here?

hanging basket

butterflies

grandma

plant

cat

lady

Harry's Hammer

Harry loves to hammer things. He hammers nails into the garden gate, and pieces of wood into the ground. Sometimes he gets carried away, and hammers people's legs, or his sandwich, and his mummy has to tell him off.

But what Mummy doesn't realise is that Harry has a magic hammer. He tries to use it as often as he can, because it makes magical things happen. It may look like an ordinary hammer, but Harry knows different...

On Tuesday, Harry says he will mend the dog kennel. He makes sure Rufus the dog is inside so they can share the adventure together. Sure enough, as he hammers the wooden slats, his hammer begins to sparkle and they are transported far away.

Rufus runs alongside Harry as they race through a prehistoric jungle. Speedy dinosaurs flash past them, but Harry and Rufus just laugh. They climb high into the trees to say hello to the tallest animals.

On Saturday, Harry goes camping. As he hammers the tent pegs into the ground, he gets that sparkling feeling again. He looks around, and the campsite has disappeared. In its place is a desert, with camels and sand dunes!

When Harry gets back to his real tent, he and Rufus sit down for a rest. Mummy calls out to them. 'Harry! Bring your hammer and help me put your go-kart together.' How exciting – another adventure!

Read these words again

far   tent

help   sand

dog   rest

wood   often

gate   mend

away   race

past   jungle

What can you see here?

dinosaur

sandwich

hammer

tent

palm tree

camel

The Tooth Pixie

Poppy hated cleaning her teeth. It was so BORING! Each night, she would turn on the tap, squirt toothpaste down the plughole, and then run out of the bathroom. Her teeth were never clean.

One night, as Poppy turned off the tap, she heard a voice. 'Do it properly!' Poppy stared in surprise at a little man, perched on the side of the bathtub. 'I think you need my help!' said the man.

The little man had pointy ears and gleaming white teeth. He jumped up onto Poppy's shoulder and whispered in her ear. 'If you don't clean your teeth, I will steal all your biscuits!' he said.

Poppy didn't believe him. She laughed, and did her usual trick of pretending to clean her teeth. Then she rushed into her bedroom and hid under the covers.

The next day, Poppy's dad handed over her lunchbox. 'No biscuits today,' he said. 'There are none left in the cupboard. I don't know how we've run out so quickly.'

That night, Poppy brushed her teeth for two minutes, until they were sparkling clean. The little man nodded in approval. 'Very good,' he chuckled. 'But I'll be watching you! You can't hide from the Tooth Pixie!'

Read these words again

night   shoulder
plughole   biscuits
bathroom   pretending
clean   usual
voice   cupboard
properly   quickly
believe   watching

What can you see here?

teddy

lamp

mirror

pixie

toothbrushes

duck

To the Rescue!

Rory was a firefighter. He went to work in a bright red fire truck. He loved putting out fires and helping in emergencies. His favourite thing was rescuing people from very tall buildings.

Rory's fire truck had a long ladder that extended up and up, high into the air. Rory would race up to the top with his hosepipe and squirt strong jets of water everywhere.

Rory worked with a firefighter called Cassie. Today, they were doing a fire drill. They drove to the park in the middle of town. Rory parked beneath the old oak tree, while Cassie opened up the ladder until it reached the top.

The children cheered as Cassie climbed up each rung of the ladder. They loved to watch the fire officers practise all of their safety operations. Rory kept watch below to make sure that Cassie was safe.

As Cassie reached the highest point of the ladder, she shouted down to Rory. 'I've found something!' She carefully leaned forward and picked a small helicopter out of the oak branches.

'It's my toy!' gasped Millie, down on the ground. 'It flew there last week and got stuck! Ooh, please can you rescue it for me?' Rory and Cassie smiled. Even fire drills have happy endings!

Read these words again

bright	endings
water	rescue
please	safety
forward	highest
ladder	beneath
ground	helicopter
branches	buildings

174

What can you see here?

helmet

hose

swings

roundabout

fire engine

flames

175

Making Magic

Alfonso was practising his latest spell. He was trying to turn his toy soldier into a real life soldier who could run and climb and keep guard in his bedroom.
It wasn't going very well.

Every time Alfonso said the magic words, a puff of dirty green smoke appeared, and the soldier fell over. Alfonso sighed and propped him up again, and recited the spell one more time.

The spell still didn't work, so Alfonso laid his wand next to the soldier, and went down for his supper. When he came back upstairs, he stopped outside his bedroom door. He could hear strange noises.

He peeped around the door and gasped. All of his toy soldiers were marching in line! They paraded up and over his drawers, along his windowsill, and across his bed. Alfonso was amazed.

Alfonso crept into his room. His marching soldiers were great fun, but he needed to make them stop. He waved his wand and muttered some words. A puff of blue smoke came out and his cars all zoomed across the floor.

Help! This was all going wrong. Alfonso took a deep breath. He read his spell very carefully and pronounced each word loudly. He waved his wand...and silence fell on his room. Phew!

Read these words again

magic   silence

smoke   loudly

dirty   sighed

supper   bedroom

upstairs   guard

wrong   soldier

drawers   paraded

What can you see here?

space mobile

toy cars

sock

magic book

shelves

soldier

Can you find these images?

bag

monster

girl

juice

sign

crisps

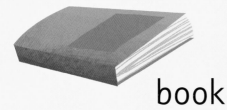

train

baby
dinosaur

book

wizard

ladder

Read these words again

new

past

declares

graceful

clever

meadow

outside

forehead

spiral

vet

crowds

pleaded

cookie

asleep

Read these words again

clothes

purple

curtains

heard

eye

daze

stumbled

lovingly

kicked

tear

faraway

money

ground

floor

Look for these objects!

Look for the dinosaur bones!

Can you find the rainbow?

Did you see what story this black cat was in?

188

Can you find
the pink unicorn?

Look for
this picture!

Where did you
see this robot?